The
Official
Barbie
ANNUAL

£5.99

This Barbie™ Annual belongs to

Catherine

Name: catherine AnnaStowers ....

Age: 4.5 ....

Address: ....

....

....

My favourite Barbie® doll is .....barbie doll...........

Written by Caroline Brook.
Designed by Paul Brunton, Primary Design.
Published by Grandreams Ltd., 435-437 Edgware Road, Little Venice, London W2 1TH.

Contents

A Special Message from Barbie 6

Barbie and a Very Special Garden 8

Get Growing! 14

Valentine's Day 16

A Valentine Card to Make 18

Summer Holiday Adventure 20

A Very Special Album 26

Where in the World? 28

Boat Trips to the Islands 29

Team Work 30

Hopes and Dreams 36

Birthdays 38

Funny Faces 40

What Do You Know About Barbie? 42

Barbie Rides in Style 44

Make a Rosette 50

The Story of Rapunzel 52

The Winter Show 54

A Special Time for Barbie 60

Answers 61

A Special Message from Barbie

Hi there!

I want to welcome you to my new annual. I'm really excited about the stories, features and puzzles you'll find inside. I hope you enjoy reading them as much as I enjoyed collecting them for you, my special friends.

I had a great year. In spring I helped Skipper and her friends with a very special project, then in summer I took a holiday in Fiji. It was supposed to be a chance to relax after all my hard work at the spring fashion shows, but the plane flight turned out to be quite an adventure!

Another adventure started when I took my dog, Ginger, for a walk in the local woods. Later in the year I had some great fun with some of my favourite two and four-legged friends. You can read about it on page 44.

We ended a great year with a special Winter Ice Show. The photograph shows me wearing one of the outfits I designed specially for the show. Do you like it?

Now, are you ready for some fun? Turn the page, and enjoy the first story – and the rest of the annual.

Love from your special friend,

6

SEEDS

My Favorite Things Love, Barbie

Barbie and a Very Special Garden

It was a lovely spring afternoon when Barbie got home from a fashion shoot. She went into the kitchen and poured herself a long drink of cool fruit juice. "Do you want some, Skipper?" she asked her sister.

Skipper was staring down at the kitchen table. She didn't look up from her school book. "Huh? What did you say?" she mumbled.

Barbie sat down beside Skipper and closed the book gently. "You're miles away, Skipper," Barbie said. "Is anything wrong?"

Skipper paused, then looked up. "Well, not wrong exactly," she said. "You see, we've been given a special school project to do, and..."

"Sounds interesting," said Barbie. "So what's the problem? Why the long face?"

"The project is based on a piece of waste ground near school," Skipper explained. "We have to work as a class and come up with an idea for how the land can be used. Something for the whole community." Skipper paused. "And we don't have one good idea between us. Not one! Do you have any ideas, Barbie?"

Barbie loves gardening. One of the projects she was working on was a new design for her garden. She had been working hard drawing plans and choosing colours. So it wasn't surprising that one of her own hobbies gave her the perfect idea for Skipper's class project!

"Why not make a garden on the waste ground? Not a private one for the school, with fences, but an open area that everyone can share and enjoy?"

"Now why didn't we think of that!?" said Skipper. "It's the perfect idea, Barbie. It's something we can all work on, and it is something people of all ages can enjoy."

"And it will be good fun!" said Barbie.

"There's just one problem," said Skipper. "We're not exactly experts when it comes to planning gardens and growing things. We're going to need a bit of help, someone to plan things and get us organized. How about it, Barbie? Will you help?"

Barbie smiled. "Of course I will," she said. "When do we start?"

The answer was – the very next day! Skipper and all her

school friends took Barbie to the piece of ground. "It's a bit of a mess now," said Barbie, "but we'll soon change all that."

Barbie soon had Skipper and her school friends working hard. First they had to clear away all the weeds, stones and litter. That alone filled quite a few wheelbarrows! Then they got rid of all the long grass and dug over the soil. Last of all they made the earth smooth and flat.

"That's all the hard work done," said Barbie. "Now for the fun part!"

Barbie drew a plan of how the garden was going to look. Skipper and her friends used the plan to mark where the paths and flower beds would go. Then they laid new grass and made paths of small stones and gravel.

Barbie took some of the children to a garden centre in her four-wheel drive. She told the owner all about the garden. He thought it was a great idea, and he gave them lots of bushes, trees and plants. He gave them flower seeds to grow, and bulbs to plant, too.

Barbie was really grateful. "You're very kind," Barbie told him. "I'll do a hanging basket demonstration for your customers as my way of saying thank you."

Soon the ground started to look like a garden. Local people were interested in what was going on, and stopped to chat and ask Skipper and her friends what they were doing. They were glad to see the waste ground being put to good use.

Barbie had thought very carefully about the garden. She explained her ideas as it took shape. "These bushes will soon grow into a thick hedge," she told Skipper and her friends as they planted them. "They will be good shelter for birds and small animals, and the berries are good for food. I've put in some bushes that insects and butterflies love, too."

Barbie wanted everyone in the area to use and enjoy the new garden. All the paths were wide enough for people pushing baby buggies, and for people in wheelchairs. There were high flower beds so they could see the flowers close up, too.

"These flowers smell lovely!" said Skipper as she planted some small plants along the edge of a path.

"Aren't they great?" said Barbie. "I chose them specially because they have such a strong scent. I want people who can't see the colours so well to enjoy the smell of the garden."

"Good idea," said Skipper. "I like the seats where elderly people can sit to rest and enjoy the garden, too."

At last the garden was finished. It looked wonderful. Skipper could hardly believe it when she compared it to photographs she'd taken of the waste ground before work began. When the last spade had been put away,

Barbie walked all around the garden. It was just as she had planned it. "It's like a painting made with flowers instead of paints," said Skipper. Barbie thought that was a lovely thing for her sister to say.

"It's all thanks to your hard work," she told Skipper and her friends. "Do you think we should do something special to open the garden?"

"We have plans for that!" said Skipper happily. "And we want you to be our special guest, Barbie. It's our way of saying thank you for helping."

Skipper and her friends made hot dogs and fizzy fruit drinks and asked everyone to the party.

Skipper tied a pink ribbon across the entrance. When Barbie cut it the garden was open. And that wasn't the only surprise. There was a special tree for Barbie to plant as a reminder of the day.

Everyone had a great time. They all agreed that the garden was a lovely place to share and enjoy. And there was one other bonus – Skipper and her school friends got top marks for making their very special garden!

Get Growing!

"Growing things is great fun, as Skipper and her friends found out when they worked on the new garden. But you can grow things even if you don't have a garden. I'll show you how to grow plants from fruit pips and seeds. You can use orange, lemon or apple seeds. Remember to ask a grown-up to help you."

You will need:

3 fruit seeds or pips

1 glass jam jar

seed potting compost

a few stones or pebbles

1 plastic bag

1 elastic band

1 old spoon

3 flowerpots

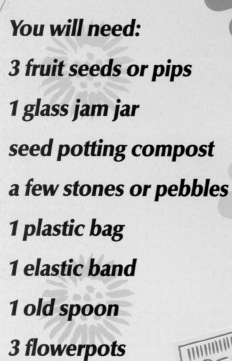

1. Put a layer of stones in the bottom of the jam jar.

2. Half fill the jar with seed potting compost. It should be damp but not wet.

3. Press the pips or seeds gently into the compost.

4. Put a plastic bag over the jam jar. Put the elastic band around the jar to keep the bag in place.

5. Put the jar in a warm place. Look at it every day. If the compost looks dry, add a little water.

6. The pips will start to grow. But you have to be patient! When they have grown into little seedlings, lift them out very carefully using a spoon.

7. Plant each seedling in a flowerpot filled with damp compost. Put the pots on a sunny window ledge. Soon they will grow into lovely little orange, lemon or apple plants!

Valentine's Day

"We had a really great time at the special Valentine's Day ball I organized with Ken. We asked all our friends to join us for a great evening of dancing and music. I'll tell you about why and how we celebrate this special day of the year."

* Lots of people send greeting cards on Valentine's Day. They are often sent secretly, without the sender's name. Many cards have little verses instead, like these:

Roses are red,
Violets are blue,
Sugar is sweet –
And so are you!

I am yours
And you are mine,
I'm glad that you're
My Valentine!

* Saint Valentine lived in Italy many, many years ago. He is the special saint of love.

* Valentine's Day is on the same date every year, February 14th.

* People used to believe that birds find their partners on February 14th every year. Some people believe it is the day when we meet special people, too.

* Valentine cards have been sent for hundreds of years. Originally they were made by the people who sent them. People drew a heart or picture on the front, and wrote a message inside.

* Valentine cards were first sold in shops about a hundred years ago. They were made by hand. They were very pretty, with tiny paper or fabric flowers, and bits of lace, ribbon and tinsel. Some had real flowers and feathers on them.

* Some cards would cost a lot of money. They had jewellery or tiny bottles of perfume or chocolates inside. Some were like little music boxes.

* You can see some of the first Valentine cards in museums.

* When the Penny Post started in 1840, cards could be sent anywhere for one old penny, much less than 1p today.

* In Great Britain the Post Office delivers about 10 million cards on Valentine's Day every year!

A Valentine Card to Make

Barbie likes getting and sending greetings cards. This year she got lots of Valentine cards, and sent some to her friends. She didn't put her name on any of them. She and her friends like to guess who sent the cards!

To make her Valentine cards extra special, Barbie makes them herself. Why don't you make some and send them to your friends on Valentine's Day? Ask a grown-up to help you.

You will need:

1 piece of white card

1 piece of bright pink card

a pencil

safety scissors

sticky tabs

silvery glitter, stars and sticky shapes

non-toxic glue

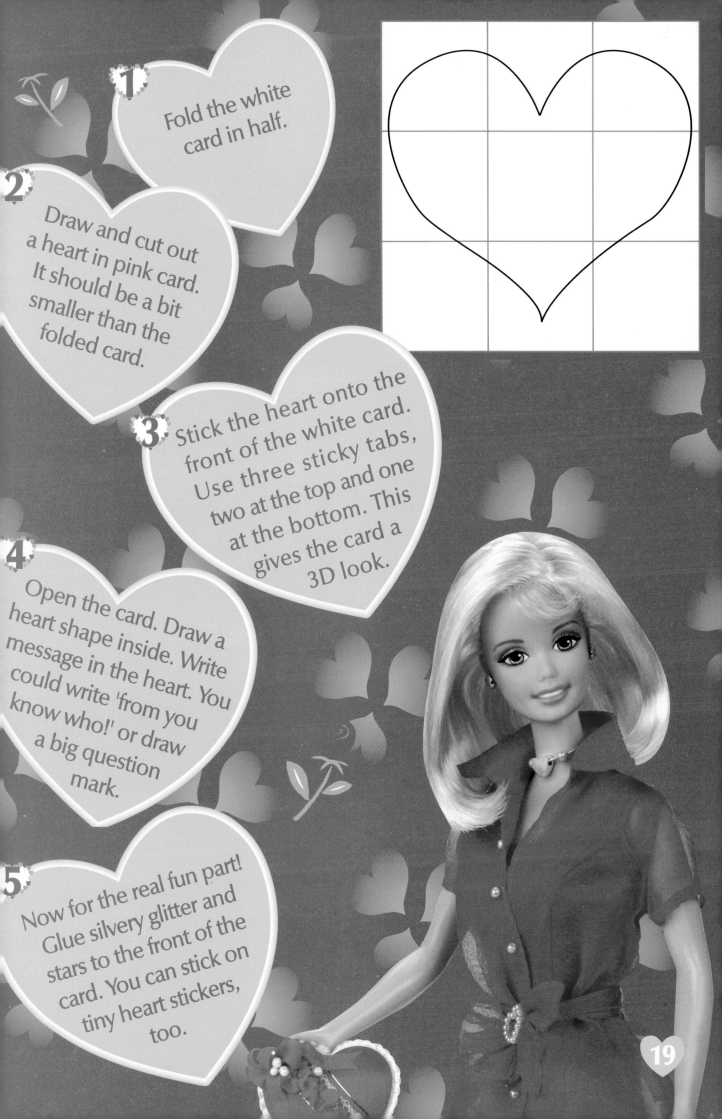

1 Fold the white card in half.

2 Draw and cut out a heart in pink card. It should be a bit smaller than the folded card.

3 Stick the heart onto the front of the white card. Use three sticky tabs, two at the top and one at the bottom. This gives the card a 3D look.

4 Open the card. Draw a heart shape inside. Write message in the heart. You could write 'from you know who!' or draw a big question mark.

5 Now for the real fun part! Glue silvery glitter and stars to the front of the card. You can stick on tiny heart stickers, too.

19

Summer Holiday Adventure

Barbie and her friend Kira were feeling really excited! They had had a busy time modelling the spring fashion collections. The big shows in Paris, Rome and London were over at last, and what they wanted now was a rest.

"Let's have a holiday," said Kira. "I think we deserve it!"

Barbie had to agree. They had worked hard modelling new clothes with the top photographers. The work is fun and exciting, but being a model is also quite hard. Pictures of Barbie and Kira had been in newspapers and magazines all over the world. That's why they decided to go somewhere peaceful. They chose the lovely islands of Fiji.

"We've spent too much time in front of a camera lens!" laughed Barbie as she and Kira packed their bags at the end of the last show. "I'm going to spend the holiday taking photographs, not posing for them!" Barbie is a really keen photographer. She was looking forward to taking loads of shots of Fiji.

Barbie and Kira spent a day at the shopping mall and came home carrying lots of bags and boxes. Inside were super new holiday outfits. Most of them were for the beach, but Barbie and Kira had new outfits to wear on the long plane journey to Fiji, too. They chose comfortable clothes made of cool, natural fabrics.

The flight to Fiji was a long one and Barbie settled down to enjoy it. She had fruit drinks to keep her cool and a good book to read.

The passengers soon settled down and everyone was quiet – apart from the little girl who was sitting right behind Barbie. She sounded a little bit upset and Barbie felt sorry for her. Barbie thought it might be her first plane trip. Perhaps Barbie could help take her mind off the flight.

Barbie was just about to say hello to the little girl when an air hostess arrived to answer the call button. She spoke to the little girl and her mother. Barbie could not help but overhear. "Ma'am, are you all right?" the hostess said. "You don't look at all well."

Barbie didn't hear an answer apart from a low moan of pain, which she guessed was from the

little girl's mother. The little girl started to cry.

The hostess went to the front of the plane and made an appeal for help. "Is there a doctor on the plane?" she asked. "One of the passengers is feeling rather unwell. Can anyone help?"

Barbie rose to her feet and spoke to the little girl. "Don't worry," she said. "I'm a doctor. I can help."

"It's Mummy!" said the little girl. Her mother was slumped in her seat with her eyes closed. "She's sick. Please help her."

Barbie was grateful for her medical training. She always carried her medical kit because as she had found in the past, you just never know when it might be needed.

Barbie soon had things under control. Kira took care of the little girl, while Barbie took care of her mother. She helped her to the back of the plane where she could lie down across the seats.

"I think it's some sort of food poisoning," Barbie told the hostess. "I've given her something to help, but we must make sure she has lots to drink. Get the pilot to ask for an ambulance to meet us at the airport and take her to hospital. And don't worry – she's going to be all right!"

"That's great news," said the air hostess. "I'm so glad you were on this flight, I really am."

Barbie looked after the woman for the rest of the flight. She kept an eye on the little girl, too, in case she had picked up the same bug, but the little girl seemed quite well. She was just worried about her mother.

Word got around the plane about what was happening. When they landed the passengers thanked Barbie as they left the plane. "We're glad you were on board to help," said one.

The ambulance staff carried the woman off the plane on a special stretcher. Barbie didn't leave until the other passengers had all gone. She was surprised to see the passengers still in the airport terminal. They clapped and cheered as she went inside!

Barbie made sure the little girl and her mother were in good hands, then she looked at her watch. "We have a little time before the car is due to pick us up," said Barbie. "Shall we change into fresh clothes?"

"Great idea!" said Kira. Barbie chose a long skirt and top, which she wore with her hair swept up on top. When she went back into the VIP lounge she found it full of television cameras and newspaper reporters. They had heard about what happened on the

plane, and now they all wanted to talk to her.

Barbie was pleased to talk to the press. "But please ignore us for the rest of the week!" she laughed. The reporters were only too glad to agree.

Barbie and Kira had a really great holiday. They spent time relaxing by the pool and on the beach. They did plenty of scuba diving and snorkelling, too. Barbie took lots of shots using a special underwater camera.

Barbie and Kira even had their hair braided and beaded as a special reminder of their holiday in Fiji.

On their last morning

on the island Barbie and Kira were waiting at the airport when Barbie saw the little girl from the plane.

"Thank you for being kind to my mummy," she said.

Her mother added her own thanks. "Thanks to you, I was out of hospital in a couple of days. We can't thank you enough."

"I'm glad you're feeling better," said Barbie.

"The plane is boarding now," said Kira. "Have you got everything, Barbie? Tickets, passport, flight bag..."

"All here," said Barbie. "And, of course, my medical kit. You just never know when I might need it!"

24

A Very Special Album

*Barbie took lots of photographs on her summer holiday in Fiji.
She enjoys taking photographs of her friends and family right through
the year. She chooses the best shots and puts them in a special album.
Here are some of her favourite photographs
Barbie wants to share with you.*

Ken and Tommy

Ken and his new baby brother, Tommy. Don't they make an adorable pair? I think Tommy is going to be just as handsome as Ken when he grows up.

I took this photograph of Shelly in her special high chair. She feels really grown up at meal times, sitting at the dining table with the rest of us.

Shelly

Stacie and friends

I wanted to do something really special for Stacie's birthday party this year. She's growing up really fast! Skipper and I decided to give her a party with a difference — a pyjama party! It was real good fun and Stacie and her friends said they had the best time ever.

Skipper is growing up fast, too. This is one of a whole lot of photographs I took of her this summer. I call it Cool Teen Skipper. What do you think of her outfit? Isn't it great?

Skipper and friends

Where in the World?

Barbie loved her holiday in Fiji. Where do you go on holiday? Do you stay near home or travel to far away places? Barbie thinks both kinds of holiday are fun.

Can you match the names of the holiday places near the bottom of the page to the countries on the world map?

North America
South America
United Kingdom
Africa
Australia

Check your answers on page 61.

Boat Trips to the Islands

One of the things Barbie and Kira enjoyed most on holiday were the boat trips they took to tiny islands. How many boats can you count on this page?

The answer is on page 61.

29

Team Work

One warm summer's day Barbie set off for a walk in the wood with her dog, Ginger. It was cool and shady out of the sun, but Ginger was hot. Barbie decided to let her cool off in the stream that ran along the far edge of the trees.

Barbie and Ginger walked deep into the wood. It was so quiet! The only sounds they could hear were bird song and the tread of their feet in the undergrowth. Barbie has travelled all over the world, but the wood is one of her favourite places. She felt lucky to have such a lovely place so close by.

Barbie and Ginger came to a part of the wood that had fewer trees. "It's not far to the stream now," Barbie said to Ginger, who was really panting hard now.

"You can take a dip when we get there."

As she walked out of the trees Barbie was surprised to see three men. One had a camera, and one held a tape measure. The third man had a big pot of red paint and a brush. "This one is coming down," Barbie overheard him say as he painted a red cross on a tall fir tree.

Barbie wondered what they were doing. When Ginger ran close to the man with the paint, he stopped and patted the dog. Barbie took the chance to say hello. "I'm surprised to see you here," said Barbie. "Ginger and I usually have the wood to ourselves!"

"I'm afraid you won't have it to yourselves for much longer," said the man.

"Why's that?" asked Barbie.

The man explained that a lot of the trees were going to be cut down. There were plans for a big new office building. "The trees with red crosses on them are going to be cut down," he said.

"That is such a shame!" said Barbie.

When Barbie took Ginger home she found that Skipper and Ken were waiting for her.

Barbie told them what was going to happen to the trees. "It's such a pity," she said. "I'm sure there are

31

other places where the offices could be built."

"I'm sure you're right," said Ken. "Why don't we try to persuade the owners to build somewhere else?"

"Yes, let's do that," said Skipper. "We'll work on it together. We'll make a great team. But where do we start?"

Barbie had lots of ideas about that! She got busy with her camera, and took lots of photographs of the woods.

Skipper took a big sketch pad and pencils into the wood. She drew lots of maps and diagrams. Then she painted two pictures. "One picture shows what the wood looks like now," she told her big sister. "And the other picture shows what it will look like after the offices are built."

Ken used the video camera to make a short film report. Barbie

wrote the script and presented it.

When Skipper told her friends about the wood, they wanted to help, too. They told local people what was happening and collected all the names of people who wanted to save the wood.

Barbie, Ken and Skipper sent their film and photographs and paintings to the head of the company that planned to build the offices.

The next day there was a message for Barbie on her telephone answering machine. It was from the head of the company, and he wanted to see the gang right away.

"We'll go and see him right now," said Barbie. "I bet he's hopping mad!"

But he wasn't!

Barbie, Ken and Skipper were taken into an office on the top floor of a tall building. It was as big as a ballroom! The photographs of the wood were spread out on a big desk.

Barbie had expected the head of the company to be wearing a frown. But he had a big smile on his face instead! "I'm so pleased to meet you," he said.

Barbie could not help looking surprised. "We thought you'd be angry," she said.

"I'm not at all angry," he replied. "I'm grateful that you let me know what was going to happen to the wood. I see lots of plans, and I don't study them as carefully as I should do."

Skipper had a big smile on her face. "So you won't be cutting the trees down?" she asked.

"No, not one," he said. He

unrolled a large plan on his desk, and pointed with his finger. "You're not the only ones who have been busy," he said. "I've found another site for the offices. It's on a site that's been used for dumping rubbish. We'll build there – and make sure we plant lots of trees, too."

"This is great, sir!" said Ken. "Thanks a million!"

"I should thank you," he said. "You three helped stop me making a big mistake."

Barbie, Skipper and Ken hurried home. They wanted to tell all the others who had helped them that the wood was safe.

Later that afternoon, they were still celebrating. "Well done, you two!" Barbie said to Ken and Skipper. "We showed that working together gets results, didn't we?"

"Yes, we make a great team," said Ken.

"The best!" Skipper agreed, then she paused. "You know, I've been thinking about the new sports centre that was going to be built. It's not even started. Do you think we can do anything about that?"

Barbie laughed. "Get your video, Ken, and hand me my camera!" she said. "Here we go again!"

My Favorite Things Love, Barbie

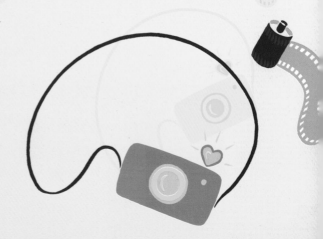

Hopes and Dreams

Barbie has lots of dreams and things she would like to do in the future.
Here are some of the things Barbie dreams of.
Why not add a dream of your own?
Write about it, or draw a picture in the empty heart shape
on the opposite page.

My Hopes and Dreams

Birthdays

Barbie gets excited about birthdays. She likes to celebrate her special day every year in style.

She likes to make everyone else's birthdays special days, too. She tries to choose gifts that are special to the month.

Why not match the next gift you give to the birthday month? The list of lucky gem stones, colours, flowers and numbers on the opposite page will help you.

month	lucky stones	lucky colours	lucky flower	lucky numbers
January	garnet	dark red	carnation	3, 7
February	amethyst	electric blue	violet	4, 8
March	bloodstone; aquamarine	lavender, purple	jonquil	5, 8
April	diamond	red, orange	sweet pea	6, 7
May	emerald	beige, cream	lily of the valley	1, 9
June	pearl	pale blue, black	rose	3, 4
July	ruby	silver, deep green	larkspur	3, 8
August	sardonyx; peridot	gold, orange	gladiolus	5, 9
September	sapphire	browns, earth	aster	4, 8
October	opal	blue	calendula	6, 9
November	topaz	sea blue, green	chrysanthemum	3, 5
December	turquoise	red	narcissus	2, 9

Funny Faces

Barbie made some funny face eats for her little sisters, Stacie and Shelly. Why don't you try making some, too? They're fun to make – and even more fun to eat!

Wash your hands before you begin, and wear an apron to keep your clothes clean. Remember – always have a grown-up to help you in the kitchen.

You will need:

1 bread roll (sometimes

called barm cakes or baps)

cottage cheese

1 tomato

1 apple

1 mushroom

salad cress

1. Ask a grown-up to cut the bread roll across the middle. Place one half so that the cut side faces up.

2. Ask a grown-up to cut 2 slices of tomato, and a slice of apple. Ask them to cut a mushroom in half.

3. Put about 3 tablespoons of cottage cheese onto the 'face'. Smooth it flat.

4. Now for the fun part – making the faces. Use cress for hair. Use the tomato slices for eyes, and a mushroom half for a nose. The piece of apple makes a smiley mouth.

You can make lots and lots of different funny faces using different foods. Here are some ideas, but you can make up your own, too.

· Use cream cheese instead of cottage cheese for the base.
· Make fruity features. Use banana slices for eyes, a grape for a nose, and an orange segment for a mouth.

· Use salad greens and pieces of lettuce for hair.
· Use carrot or radish slices for eyes or a nose.

What Do You Know About Barbie?

How much do you know about Barbie and her friends and family? Find out by answering these questions.

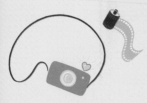

The answers are on page 61.

1. Ken has a baby brother. What is his name?

Question 1.

2. What is the name of the friend who went on holiday to Fiji with Barbie?

Question 3.

3. What kind of animals are Stomper, Nibbles, Prancer and Midnight?

4. Barbie is a top skater. In which country were the 1998 Winter Olympics held?

5. Barbie has three sisters, Skipper, Stacie, and who else?

Question 4.

Question 5.

6. Barbie has a middle name that begins with the letter M. What is it?

Question 2.

7. What is the surname of Ken?

8. What kind of pets are Honey and Tag Along Tiffy?

43

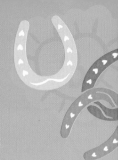

Barbie Rides in Style

Barbie is a top model, and she is always busy. Her diary is usually full, so she likes to make the best of her days off. She likes to get away from the jet set life and spend time doing things that are very different from modelling.

One of her favourite things to do on a free day is help out at the local riding stables. She keeps her own horses there so that they can be well looked after even when she is away from home. But Barbie looks after them herself whenever she can. As every pony-mad young girl knows, looking after ponies and horses is all part of the fun of owning and riding them.

Barbie always likes to look her best, and that includes the time she spends at the stables. She has a great collection of riding clothes. She likes to ride in style.

When Barbie visits the stables she likes to groom her horses and give their hooves a polish. She sometimes plaits and braids their manes and tails, too. They seem to enjoy the attention they get! One thing she always takes with her is a big bag of apple and carrot pieces as a special treat. The horses have come to expect it now!

Barbie is an expert rider and trainer, and she enjoys schooling her own horses. She likes working with the younger horses, too. Barbie knows that being patient and kind works best.

Another thing Barbie enjoys is helping with special riding lessons for disabled children. Children who can't walk can be helped to ride. Riding builds their confidence, and makes them feel special. And the horses and ponies seem to love their visits!

One of the young girls who never misses her riding lesson is Becky. She usually gets around in a wheelchair, but only when she can't ride a horse instead! Barbie and Becky have spent lots of time together at the stables and have become very good friends.

The two of them were chatting at the end of a lesson as Barbie helped Becky to rub down the pony she had been riding. Becky told Barbie that her mum had bought her a new book all

about horses. "I've been reading about the famous horses at the Vienna Riding School in Austria," said Becky. "They're great! They're all white, and they have been trained to do the most amazing leaps. I wish I could see one of their shows."

Vienna is a long way away, so a visit wasn't possible, but Becky's words gave Barbie an idea... And when Barbie has an idea, things soon start to happen!

When Becky and the others had gone home, Barbie had a word with her friend Kira, who also has a horse at the stables. They chatted for a while. "Well, what do you think?" asked Barbie.

"I think you've had another one of your brilliant ideas, Barbie!" said Kira. "The kids will love it!"

"But can we do it?" said Barbie.

"Of course we can," said Kira. "I'll help, and the grooms and riders will want to take part, too."

"Please remember, it has got to be kept a secret," said Barbie. "If the kids hear of it, it will spoil the surprise."

"It's our secret," replied Kira. "Now, let's get practising. We've got a lot of work to do!"

Barbie, Kira and their friends were soon hard at work. There were lots of things to plan and get ready for the big day.

That day finally came, and Barbie and the others had a big surprise for Becky and her friends, who thought they were just going to have their usual lesson.

But instead, Barbie and Kira had planned a horse and pony show, starring Barbie and her riding friends. They wore special outfits that Barbie had designed herself. Barbie and the others had worked really hard with the horses. They trotted and galloped around the arena in time to music. Some of them even did fancy leaps high into the air! Barbie gave a display of carriage driving. She drove a little carriage pulled by six tiny miniature ponies.

Becky and the others all cheered and clapped when Barbie and her friends put on games and had races that both the horses and ponies seemed to enjoy as much as they did. There was a very exciting show jumping contest, too.

The show ended with all the riders taking part in a special procession

46

around the arena, as the children stamped and cheered and clapped. "I know you wanted to see the white horses in Vienna," Barbie whispered to Becky as she stopped in front of her to take a bow. "I hope the show wasn't a disappointment."

"It was great!" said Becky. "It was even BETTER than going to Vienna!"

Soon the arena was empty. Before everyone went home Barbie thanked them for coming, and thanked Kira and her friends for helping her put on the show. There was so much clapping that Barbie could hardly hear herself speak!

Barbie had one last surprise for the guests. She had made little rosettes for them all to remind them of the show. Barbie thinks of everything!

Make a Rosette

"You can make a rosette badge just like the ones I made for Becky and her friends. I'll show you how. Remember to ask a grown-up to help you."

You will need:

card

safety scissors

sticky tape

felt-tip pens

1 safety pin

Step 1.

1. Draw and cut out a card circle. It should measure about 8cm across. You could draw around a small tumbler or mug.

Step 2.

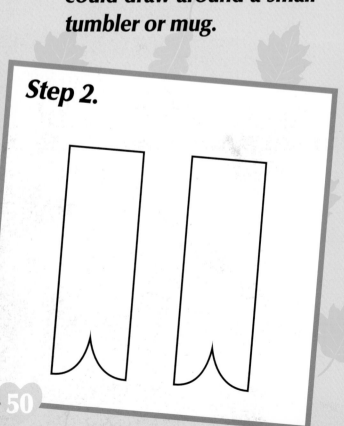

2. Cut out 2 strips of card 6cm long and 2cm wide. Cut one end of each piece to make a banner shape.

3. Stick the 2 card strips to the back of the card circle, using sticky tape. They should look like the ribbons on a rosette.

4. Decorate the rosette using felt-tip pens. Don't forget to colour the ribbon!

5. Leave the middle plain. Write a message like '1st prize friend' or 'top sister'.

6. Stick a safety pin to the back of the rosette using sticky tape.

Wear the badge pinned to your clothes, or use a sticky tab to put it on your bedroom wall.

Finished!

Top Sister

The Story of Rapunzel

"Do you know the story of Rapunzel and the handsome prince? It is one of my favourites, and very romantic. When Ken and I were asked to plan a special ball, we decided on a fairy story theme. I designed special costumes for us. I was Rapunzel and Ken was the handsome prince. I'll tell you the story."

Long ago there lived a man and his wife. Their house was next to a garden where crisp salad leaves grew. "I must have some of those leaves," said the wife.

Her husband went to get her some. But the owner was a witch! "You can take the leaves," said the witch. "But in return you must give me your daughter Rapunzel when she is twelve years old." The man was very frightened, so he agreed.

The years passed and the man forgot his promise.

But the witch did not. When Rapunzel was twelve the witch put her in a tall tower in a forest. It had no stairs or doors, just a small window right at the top.

When the witch called, "Rapunzel, let down your golden hair," the girl let down her long hair for the witch to use as a ladder.

One day a handsome prince heard Rapunzel's sweet voice. He decided to rescue her.

Every day he brought silk, and Rapunzel used it to make a ladder that grew and grew.

But the witch found out about the prince. She cut off Rapunzel's long hair and sent her far away. She put a spell on the prince's eyes so that he could not see.

The prince could not find Rapunzel until one day he heard her singing and followed her voice.

Rapunzel started to cry when she saw the prince. When two of her tears touched his eyes, he could see again!

The handsome prince took Rapunzel to his castle, where they lived happily ever after.

The Winter Show

Barbie has a favourite charity. It's one she started herself, to help make the dreams of sick or unhappy children come true.

Letters to the charity arrive from all over the world, and Barbie reads every one. She is amazed by some of the things the children want to do. One little girl wanted to go to the moon. That was a tricky one, even for Barbie! She took the little girl to a special museum to see spaceships that really had been to the moon. She even got to try on a spacesuit!

Barbie has a special young friend called Becky. Her legs don't work so well, so she has to use a wheelchair to get around. But she doesn't let that stop her from having fun in life. She enjoys doing the same sort of things that all kids enjoy.

Becky's favourite time of the year is Christmas. One year when Barbie met up with her at the riding stables Barbie asked what she wanted for Christmas. Becky didn't need to think twice – she knew exactly what she wanted. It wasn't a gift, but a special trip. "Where to?" asked Barbie. "An African safari maybe?"

"No, nothing like that!" said Becky. "I want to go to the North Pole, to meet Father Christmas! And I'd like to take some friends with me. That would be my Christmas gift to them."

"That is quite a dream!" said Barbie.

Barbie decided to try to make Becky's dream come true. She talked about it with Ken, and they worked out a plan. They knew that Becky and her friends couldn't go to visit Father Christmas at the North Pole – but Father Christmas could come to visit them. And this wasn't going to be any ordinary visit. Barbie and Ken planned something

really special...

Barbie got in touch with her friends, who all help out with her projects. She told them about the plan. "We're going to put on a very special show," she told everyone. "There's going to be dancing and singing with a winter theme – all performed on ice skates!"

The others couldn't wait to get started!

Barbie and her sister Skipper designed special outfits for the show. They chose cool winter pastel colours as their theme, to match the outdoor ice stage that Barbie had set up in the grounds of her home.

Ken had a very important job. He designed some great strobe lighting that made it look as if a million snowflakes were falling gently from the dark night sky onto the ice, which shone and glittered with thousands of tiny sequins.

Ken also arranged the music for the songs that Barbie and Skipper and two friends were going to sing as a group.

The night of the show was just perfect. The sky was like black velvet studded with a million stars. Barbie had told Becky and her friends to come dressed in warm clothing for a surprise evening, so they didn't know what to expect. Helpers showed them to their seats

in the darkness... and then Ken's lights lit up the ice stage and the sky above it. The audience gasped in amazement – it was quite a sight!

The show got off to a really great start with Barbie and Skipper's singing group, who looked great in their pastel outfits plus silvery glitter in their hair and make-up. They sounded even better, and soon had Becky and her friends clapping and singing with them.

There were some amazing ice skating displays and for one special dance and music routine Ken had set up a wonderful firework display!

At the end of a great show the lights went right down, and Barbie asked for silence. Becky and the rest of the guests all squealed with delight as they heard the ring of sleigh bells and the clip-clop of hooves getting nearer and nearer! They held their breath as the lights suddenly came on again and gasped as on to the stage came Barbie dressed as the Ice Queen, all in glittering, shimmering white. She led out, not reindeer, but Skipper

and her friends! They pulled a glittering sleigh with hundreds of pastel coloured balloons tied to the back of it. It was piled high with presents.

Sitting on the sleigh and waving to the audience was a figure dressed all in red with a long white beard. It was Father Christmas!

But was it really him? Becky smiled at her friend sitting next to her. "He's a bit too handsome to be the real Father Christmas!" said Becky happily. I wonder who it could have been? Can you guess?

A Special Time for Barbie

"*I love the special time when one year ends
and another begins.
It's a time to look back over the past year – and to
look ahead to the new one.
I have lots of hopes for the new year, and I bet you
do, too. Lots of new things will happen – maybe
you'll move house, start a new school, make new
friends or take up a new sport or hobby.
Whatever 1999 has in store for you,
I hope it will be a happy and successful year.
Goodbye, and I hope to meet you
in next year's annual!*

Love from your special friend

Answers

Where in the World?
(page 28)

1 United Kingdom
2 Africa
3 North America
4 Australia
5 South America

Boat Trips to the Islands
(page 29)

There are 11 boats.

What Do You Know About Barbie? (page 42)

1 Tommy
2 Kira
3 They are all horses and ponies
4 Japan
5 Shelly
6 Millicent
7 Carson
8 They are kittens